HOW TO DRAW

THE NEWEST

POKéMON

FEATURING SINNOH CHARACTERS

By Maria B. Alfano

ISBN-13: 978-0-545-02620-8
ISBN-10: 0-545-02620-2

12 11 10 9 8 7 6 5 4 3 2 1   7 8 9 10 11 12/0

Printed in the USA
First printing, October 2007

SCHOLASTIC INC.
New York Toronto London Auckland Sydney
Mexico City New Delhi Hong Kong Buenos Aires

Your Pokémon Drawing Journey is About to Begin...
Train your brain to draw the newest Pokémon!
Start with basic shapes and move on to action poses,
color, and tips on making each Pokémon look 3-D!

And remember, Pokémon artists-in-training never travel alone.
In this book, you'll find 14 Pokémon to keep you company. Which one will
you draw first? Pick a Pokémon, grab a pencil, and get started!

You will need: Pencils, Paper, Eraser

You might also want: Thin Black Marker, Colored Pencils,
Markers, Crayons, Scrap Paper

Look for this Poké Ball to find top-secret drawing tips from Pokémon Drawing Experts.

Start each drawing in pencil and keep your
lines light until you're almost finished. This will
make them easier to erase or draw on top of.

WARM-UP

All drawings—even the really hard ones—start off the same way.
They start with lines and basic shapes.

To warm up your drawing arm, practice drawing different
shapes and lines. You can draw circles, ovals, rectangles,
and triangles, or squiggles, curves, straight lines, thick lines,
thin lines, and even zigzags!

GUIDELINES
Start each drawing with two lines that cross. These are called guidelines.

Guidelines can help you figure out where to place different shapes and details in your drawing. For example, the horizontal guideline can show you where to draw the shoulders and arms like in this drawing of Mime Jr.

The vertical guideline runs right down the center of a Pokémon's body—like a spine or backbone.

Are you ready to get this journey started? Artist, go!

HOW TO DRAW FACES:

Practice on Pikachu! Start by drawing a circle for Pikachu's head. Then draw two crisscrossing lines inside the circle. These guidelines will show you where to draw the eyes, nose, mouth, and ears.

Can you tell which way Pikachu's head is facing?

Guidelines on the face are curved because faces are rounded.

See how Pikachu's eyes sit just on top of the horizontal guideline? Draw one eye on each side of the vertical guideline. The vertical guideline also runs through the middle of Pikachu's mouth.

Now, draw Pikachu's nose on the spot where the two guidelines cross. Finish off your drawing with details and you're done!

MANTYKE

This friendly Pokémon looks like a mini-version of its evolved form, Mantine. Mantyke is good at special attack moves, like Water Pulse and Surf. It's also a great Pokémon to try drawing first. Mantyke's body looks like a big circle with fins. Can you tell why it's known as the Kite Pokémon?

1 Start by drawing two guidelines that crisscross and curve. Keep them really light so you can erase them later on.

2 Draw a big oval on top of the lines. The two lines meet in the middle of the oval. Then use the horizontal guideline to help you position the fins.

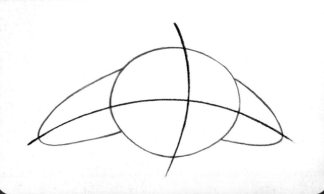

3 Use the lines from step one as a guide to place the eyes and mouth. Then draw two antenna feelers at the top of Mantyke's oval body.

4 It's time to add details! Draw the curving line that runs around Mantyke's body. Then add another line for the tongue. Finally, darken the details on Mantyke's bright happy eyes.

5 You did it! Your first Pokémon drawing is almost done. Erase the guidelines from step one and any other lines you don't need. Now, take a minute to fine-tune the outline of the body.

6 Chase away the blues . . . with color! Color in Mantyke with two different shades of blue. Then go back and trace over the lines with a thin black marker.

GREAT JOB! You've just powered through your first Pokémon drawing challenge. Keep up the good work!

PIPLUP

Piplup may be cute, but it's also one tough—and proud—Pokémon! Lots of Trainers in the Sinnoh region choose to start their Pokémon journey with this Water-type. You can choose to start your drawing training with Piplup, but here's a tip: Don't be too proud to make mistakes. You're just starting out!

1 This drawing is all about ovals. Start with two criss-crossing guidelines. Then use them to place the ovals for the head, flippers, and feet. Now draw the guidelines on the face.

2 Look at the face. The middle of the nose sits right where the two guidelines meet. Now, draw the body around the ovals you drew for the flippers and feet in step one.

Did you notice? The guidelines for Piplup's face are not in the center of the circle. That's because Piplup is not looking straight ahead!

The first two steps are about being fast and loose. Use quick, light lines!

3 Add details like Piplup's tail. Then draw curved lines on its feet for toes. Finally, darken in the eyes and add a zigzag pattern on its forehead.

4 Erase the guidelines from step one and any other lines you don't need. Congratulations! Is a cute little Piplup looking back at you?

You can turn the circle you drew for Piplup's nose into a beak by adding a wide curved line like a smile.

Did you know? Piplup have a layer of down covering their bodies to protect them from cold water and hot temperatures.

5 Color in Piplup with cool shades of turquoise and aqua. You can use a white colored pencil for Piplup's eyes and the ovals on its chest. But if you are drawing on white paper, you can just leave those areas empty.

Plip! Plop! Piplup love to splash around and play in the water. Now that you can draw Piplup, try drawing it diving into icy cold water to look for food!

MIME JR.

Mime Jr., Mimic, now! Mime Jr. likes to mimic the moves of its opponents in battle. Enemies let down their guard because they can't look away. Sometimes, it's just as hard to look away from a drawing you've been struggling with. When this happens, hold your drawing up to a mirror. Looking at it from a different perspective will help you spot mistakes.

1 The guidelines are different in this drawing. The horizontal line curves like the arms of a stick figure. Draw a big oval for the head above the arms and smaller ovals for the hands and body. At this stage, Mime Jr. should look kind of like a snowman.

2 Start with ovals for the eyes, nose, and the sides of the hat. Then, draw Mime Jr.'s body around the circle you drew in step one. See how helpful basic shapes can be?

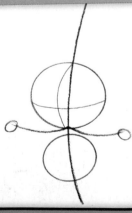
There's a lot going on in step two, but don't let it scare you off. Break it down. And take your time!

3 Almost done! Add details like a smiling mouth and dark eyes. Then draw a string of U shapes around Mime Jr.'s waist. Follow the curve of the circle so it looks 3-D.

Remember to look back to the introduction for tips on drawing faces.

4 Great job! Erase any lines you don't need. Now take a minute to look at your drawing. Do you need to make any changes?

Smudge-proof your masterpiece! Keep a piece of scrap paper under your hand as you draw.

5 Color your Mime Jr. with shades of pink, red, and blue. Don't you think Mime Jr. looks like a little clown?

Feeling good? You're ready to move on to the next level. Keep going!

PIKACHU

Pika Power! Pikachu are known for their sparkling personalities—and electrifying moves like Thunderbolt. But do you know what makes these amazing moves possible? Pikachu store an electric charge in their cheeks. Then, in times of danger or battle, the powerful charge can be released! Have you been storing up enough energy to draw this shocking Electric-type?

1 Start by drawing two lines that crisscross. Next draw a circle for the head. See how the bottom of the circle just touches the horizontal line in the cross? Now attach a squared-off U-shape for the body and ovals for the hands and feet.

Take time to set up your drawing in step one. Getting the basics down will help make the drawing easier once the steps get more complicated.

2 Draw the ears and arms. Where do you want to put the eyes and mouth? Use the criss-cross guidelines to help you figure it out. Now, take a minute to tweak the shape of Pikachu's face and body. Use the basic shapes you drew in step one to guide you.

Remember that zigzag from the warm-up? Use it to start Pikachu's tail!

3 Use zigzagging lines to add fingers. Zigzags also add detail to the tail. Then, use short quick lines to make toes. Don't forget to draw in Pikachu's nose and the circles for super-charged cheeks.

4 You're in the home stretch! Erase any lines you don't need. Now, take a good look at your drawing. Pay special attention to the outline of the body. Do you need to make any changes?

Need a jolt of energy? Try this warm-up exercise: draw 50 circles really fast. You may be shocked to discover that your circles get rounder when you draw faster.

5 Smudge-proof your Pikachu! Color in the bright yellow body first. If you're using a marker, make sure it's completely dry before placing the darker colors on top of the yellow.

MUNCHLAX

Happy to be hungry? This hyper little Pokémon loves to chow down. All. The. Time! Munchlax will do anything for food, like rummage through garbage cans, run for miles, or even stop in the middle of a Pokémon battle! Munchlax isn't as big—or as sleepy—as its evolved form, Snorlax, but you'll still need plenty of big circles and sweeping curves to draw this Pokémon.

1 Start with guidelines as usual. Then draw a big circle for the body. Finish up by adding a shape that looks like a football for the head and ovals for the hands and feet.

2 Take it slow. Start with the easier parts like the zigzags on the fingers and body. Then work on the head. Draw the jaw jutting out from the football shape you drew in step one. Then add a wide U to show the inside of the mouth. Finally, draw two ovals for eyes.

Lighten up! Keep your grip loose and move your entire arm as you draw—not just your wrist.

Think big! Start out with the big shapes. Save the details for the end.

3 Way to go! The hardest parts of the drawing are already done. Add details like upside-down V shapes for the ears, teeth, and toes. Then erase any lines you don't need.

4 Stop and take a step back from your drawing. You might even want to tape it up to the wall. Sitting too close makes it harder to spot things that need to be fixed.

Feeling as hungry as Munchlax? Healthy snacks like carrot sticks and nuts can help you stay energized and focused while drawing.

5 Now, take out your markers and get ready to color!

BONSLY

Looks can be deceiving! Bonsly may seem timid, but they're rock solid underneath it all. With strong moves like Rock Slide and Fake Tears they can charm opponents and defend themselves at the same time. And those tears aren't about being sad—or tricky. Tears help Bonsly regulate the water in their bodies when the air is really dry. This drawing may look tough, but you can handle it. Rock on!

1
You guessed it—start with guidelines. Then draw a big circle. The bottom of it should touch the horizontal guideline. Draw a smaller circle at the very top of the vertical guideline. Now, start on the feet and legs.

Don't forget the guidelines on the face!

2
Start by drawing the circles on top of Bonsly's head. Then move on to the hat and face. Bonsly has a ring around its body just below its mouth.

Ring around the Bonsly! Take a closer look at that waist area.

1 | 2 | 3

3 Draw a dark oval inside the eyes. Then draw a short curved line inside the mouth to make it look open. Now, add a football-like shape to the top of Bonsly's front leg and a U-shape at the top of its back leg. You're almost done!

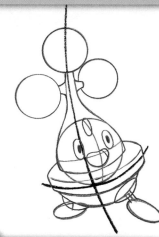

Step by Step! When a drawing looks really complicated, pick out one area that looks easier than the rest and draw that first.

4 Erase any lines you don't need—like the bottom of the circle you drew for the head. Phew! Now you can see your drawing and clean up mistakes.

Don't get teary-eyed! Mistakes help you learn and ultimately make you a better artist.

5 Want to make the balls on top of Bonsly's head look 3-D? Add a light yellow-green highlight to the top-left side of each ball and a warmer brown-green crescent-shaped shadow on the bottom right.

TURTWIG

This Grass-type Pokémon is the starter Pokémon of choice for lots of Trainers in the Sinnoh Region. It has powerful moves like Leaf Storm, and it loves living near water! Maybe that's because the shell on its back gets stronger every time it absorbs water. One thing is for sure: As an artist-in-training, you can learn a lot from Turtwig. It's brave and confident. And sometimes you have to risk making a mistake to create a great drawing.

1 Start with an oval for the head. Then attach the shape for the body. Now draw ovals for the feet. Finally, draw a big U shape up at the top of your drawing. This will become leaves later on.

2 Begin drawing the face. Then add details to the shell on Turtwig's back. Don't forget to draw the back leg. And tweak the shape of the other legs. Now, work on the leaves on top of Turtwig's head and attach them to a cone.

Time's up! Try timing yourself. Draw a Turtwig in under a minute and see what happens. You won't have time to worry about messing up! And you might end up with a masterpiece!

Don't forget to use the guidelines to help you place the different parts of your drawing, like the eyes and body.

3 Draw two lines that slant down at the top of the ovals you drew for eyes. Remember to leave an oval of white for the highlight in each eye. Now, add details to the body and legs.

When drawing eyes, make sure the highlight is in the same place in each eye. This way your Pokémon won't look cross-eyed.

4 Time to clean up your drawing! Did you draw the jaw-plate? Take a minute to redraw any parts that need fixing.

Iron grip! Whether Turtwig is attacking in battle or giving a big hug, it can use its super-strong jaw to latch onto Trainers or other Pokémon.

5 Color your creation! Shadows can help make a drawing look 3-D. They are usually warm in tone—made up of colors like reds, violets, and browns.

Here's an idea: When Turtwig gets thirsty, the leaves on top of its head wilt. Try drawing a super-thirsty Turtwig now!

AIPOM

It only takes one look at Aipom's smiling face to know this Normal-type Pokémon isn't aggressive. But it is energetic! It lives in treetops, and can leap from tree to tree all day with the help of its nimble tail. All that leaping can work up an appetite, though, so Aipom's tail also comes in handy for grabbing fruit to eat—or a branch to nap on. Having trouble with your drawings? Don't give up! Follow Aipom's lead and take a break. You'll be recharged in no time!

1 Use this step to set-up your drawing. Aipom starts with guidelines and ovals just like the other Pokémon.

2 Start with the ears. Do you see how one is partially hidden behind Aipom's head? Then use upside-down V's to draw the hair on top of Aipom's head. Now use the guidelines from step one to help you draw the arms, legs, and tail.

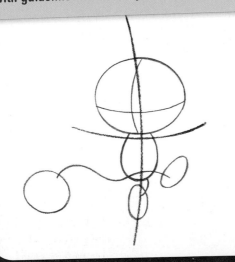

Time out! Use scrap paper to practice drawing the hand on the end of Aipom's tail. Practice is the only way to become a Pokémon drawing expert!

3 Draw short vertical lines for teeth inside Aipom's mouth. Then finish up the eyes. Draw a curved line on each foot to make toes. Now, erase any lines you don't need.

4 Clean up your drawing. Does the right leg look like it's in front of the left leg? Once you've erased all your guidelines, you're ready to move on to the next step.

It's nice to keep your early drawings —even the bad ones—so you can track how much you improve!

5 Lost your lavender color? Lay down a light shade of pink. Then add a layer of pale blue on top of it. This technique works best with colored pencils.

Here's an idea! Draw Aipom's tail reaching out to grab its favorite food—fruit!

BUIZEL

Dive in! This Water-type Pokémon has splash-tastic moves like Whirlpool and SonicBoom, and it evolves into Floatzel. Drawing Buizel may look tough, but you've been training hard. Take a cue from this playful Pokémon and have fun while you draw. You're not battling for a Gym Badge!

1 Get your guidelines ready. Then draw ovals for the head, arms, and feet. Now, connect the feet with a curved line.

2 Take it slow and break it down. You're a pro! Connect the shapes you drew in step one to draw the body. Then add a big Y-shaped tail. Can you use the guidelines to help you place the eye?

Did you know? Buizel's tail spins like a boat propeller so it can swim faster.

If you get stuck, just look at the next step to help you figure out where to put a line or detail.

3 Phew! Now it's time to have fun. Add details to the face like eyebrows and a mouth. Then use a variety of lines to add toes to the feet and patterns to the body and tail.

4 Stand back and take a good look at your drawing. Sometimes it's easier to see mistakes when you're not sitting so close. Then, clean up the outlines and get ready to color!

5 Orange you glad you finished this drawing? Now that you can draw Buizel, draw it splashing around in the water! The ring around its neck inflates like an inner tube to help it float.

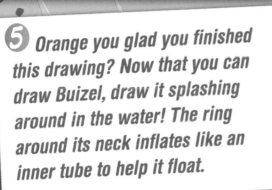

CHIMCHAR

Chimchar heat things up with moves like Flame Wheel and Fire Spin. They're also quick and nimble—they have to be to climb the rocky cliffs where they live. And if you're patient, Chimchar will evolve into Monferno. If you live in the Sinnoh region and want to start your Pokémon journey with a fiery friend, Chimchar is the Pokémon for you!

1 This Pokémon is dancing around, so start by drawing the guidelines on an angle. Then add the basic shapes for the arms, legs, hands, feet, and body.

2 Add the jaw and mouth to the bottom of the circle you drew for a head. Then place the eyes and attach basic shapes for the hair and ears. Now connect the shapes you drew in step one to create the body, legs, and arms.

Tackle those toes! They're short curved lines.

22

3 There are lots of details in this step so take your time. Use your training to draw Chimchar's eyes. Then add short quick lines for the eyebrows, nose, and teeth. The tail is also really important. Keep the flame half-hidden behind Chimchar's body.

4 Great job! Erase extra lines so you can see your drawing. Did you remember to draw the swirl on Chimchar's tummy? What about the bangs? They look like the letter M.

TAKE A CLOSER LOOK!
Practice drawing Chimchar's fists on scrap paper. You might even want to trace them a few times first. Tracing isn't cheating!

Did you know? Chimchar's tail flame only goes out when it sleeps—not when it rains like Charmander's and Cydaquil's.

5 Use warm, fiery tones like burnt orange, yellow, and red to color your creation. Keep the color lighter in the highlights.

Here's an idea! Now that you can draw Chimchar, draw your fiery friend using its Flamethrower attack!

23

WEAVILE

Weavile are mischievous Pokémon. They use their sharp claws to carve messages for one another in icy surfaces and on trees. Did you know you could carve out your own drawing style? Every drawing is different, just like every Pokémon's personality is different. What will you do to make this drawing your own? It's a super-charged Pokémon challenge, but you can do it!

1 Start with a stick figure. Draw the back leg bent and keep the front leg straight so it looks like it's coming forward. The feet and arms are triangles this time instead of ovals.

2 Step 2: Break it down! Use the center line to help you make Weavile's crown symmetrical. The oval jewel on its forehead also sits right on the centerline. Now draw the eyes and ears. They're all shaped like crescent moons!

Weavile's head is tilted down, so the horizontal guideline on the face is all the way at the bottom of the circle you drew for the head. Remember, guide-lines on the face curve.

There are lots of jagged lines in this drawing, like Weavile's sharp claws. Did you practice drawing zigzags in the warm-up?

3 Use this step to fine-tune the outlines of the shapes you drew in steps one and two. This will make Weavile look more realistic. Then draw the tail and add details like the teeth, eyelashes, and lines in the ears.

4 Compare your drawing to the Weavile in the book. Are you missing anything? Make any last minute adjustments.

TAKE A CLOSER LOOK!
Did you notice that Weavile has three claws on each paw, instead of two like Sneasel, its pre-evolved form? Practice drawing Weavile's folded arms on scrap paper.

5 Weavile's dark red eyes match its headgear and tail. But the oval on its forehead is a golden yellow. Color it in first so it doesn't get muddy.

Here's an idea: Draw a pair of Weavile in a snowy forest—where they love to live. What kind of mysterious messages have they carved on the trees?

CHATOT

Chatot is a colorful Pokémon, so get ready to work hard and have fun! This Pokémon can copy what people say, but it can't talk on its own. If you're having trouble drawing Chatot on your own, take a tip from this Normal-and-Flying-type and try copying or tracing it first to practice. Tracing is a great way to learn!

The guidelines in this drawing are big sweeping curves.

1 Draw one oval for the head and another for the body. Then, decide where you want to place the wing and lightly sketch it in.

2 Draw the feathers first. Then add the beak and claws. Now draw the tail and the flag-like shape on top of Chatot's head.

Not sure where a line is supposed to be? Take a look at the finished drawing to help you understand what to do next—or just for inspiration.

3 You're almost done! Add little details like the eyes and more feathers on the wings and legs. Did you remember to draw the circle on Chatot's tail?

4 Erase extra lines and take a good look at your drawing. Is the shape of the body correct?

Hands off! Just for fun, try drawing with your weaker hand. Maybe you'll surprise yourself with a Pokémon masterpiece!

5 Color says a lot about personality. Add black to Chatot's head and tail. Its head looks like a music note! That's because Chatot is a very musical Pokémon. Its tail can even tick out a steady beat!

Did you know? Chatot's signature move is Chatter. It totally confuses opponents!

27

LUCARIO

Lucario has strange powers. It can read thoughts! And with moves like Inner Focus and Steadfast, this Fighting-and-Steel-type Pokémon is a formidable opponent. It's also a challenging drawing, so take your time and go for it! You're a Pokémon drawing expert!

1 Start with a stick figure. It helps to figure out early on where you want to put the arms and legs.

2 Build Lucario's body around the stick figure. The back leg is smaller than the front leg because it's farther away. Now, draw the eyes, ears, and snout. Did you use jagged lines for the paws?

Remember to use light lines when you start a drawing to make it easier to erase.

3 This step is all about details—in the paws, the ears, and on the face. Practice drawing spikes on scrap paper before you add them to your drawing.

4 Look back and forth between steps three and four. Did you miss any details or forget to erase any lines? Do it now!

MAGNIFY IT!
Are all of Lucario's details driving you crazy? Take out a magnifying glass. Sometimes seeing those little lines on a larger scale can help.

Draw one short line for the knee. It's amazing what one little line can do!

5 Do you want your drawing to look 3-D? Imagine shining a bright light on Lucario. What parts would the light hit? These areas are the highlights. The parts that wouldn't get light fall into shadow.

LOOKIN' GOOD! You just finished one of the toughest drawings in this book. You're an official Pokémon drawing expert!

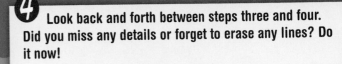

29

MANAPHY

Because this Legendary Pokémon's body is 80% water, Manaphy are highly affected by their environment. What's your drawing environment like? Is it quiet? Do you have enough space? It's a smart idea to set aside a small corner of your room where you can spend ten minutes a day drawing. You'll be surprised by how fast you gain skills. Your drawings will be legendary!

1 This drawing starts out a little differently. The horizontal guideline sweeps out in a quick V because Manaphy is spreading its arms in joy. Draw a gumdrop shape for the head and ovals for the hands and feet. Don't forget the guidelines for the face.

Did you notice? Manaphy's head is almost twice the size of its body!

2 First draw the antenna. They're squiggly lines with circles at the ends. Then draw Manaphy's flipper-like arms. Remember to use the guidelines to help you. Now place the eyes and mouth.

3 Draw the jewel-like markings on Manaphy's stomach right on the vertical guideline. Then draw two circles reaching up from each eye like eyelashes.

4 Now, make sure you're happy with the outlines and fix anything that's not quite right. Did you erase some of the lines in the antenna so it looks like one is in front of the other?

TAKE A CLOSER LOOK!
Draw an oval. Then draw two more ovals inside that one. Color in one of the smaller ovals and leave the other empty for the highlight. Voila! You just drew an eye!

5 Jump for joy! And get ready to battle color. Manaphy is blue with touches of yellow and red.

Time for teamwork! Manaphy's signature move is Heart Swap. Try starting a drawing, and then swap it with a friend halfway through. What kind of drawing will you create when you work together?

Congratulations! You're an official Pokémon Drawing Expert. Now that you can draw the newest Pokémon, your real Pokémon drawing journey can begin. Try drawing your Pokémon in the wild, or competing for the coolest new Gym Badges. Or just draw a group of them hanging out and having fun together. The choice is yours! **Go, Pokémon Artist, Go!**